£4.50

CONTENTS

Cover by Paul Gamble and John Burns

TINY TOON ADVENTURES ANNUAL 1993 is published by MARVEL
COMICS LTD., 13/15 Arundel St, London WC2R 3DX, under license from
WARNER BROS, INC.™ ©1992 Warner Bros, Inc. All rights reserved. TINY
TOON ADVENTURES, the Tiny Toons Adventures characters, their
distinctive likenesses, and all related characters, slogans and indicia are the
property and trademarks of Warner Bros Inc. Printed in Italy.

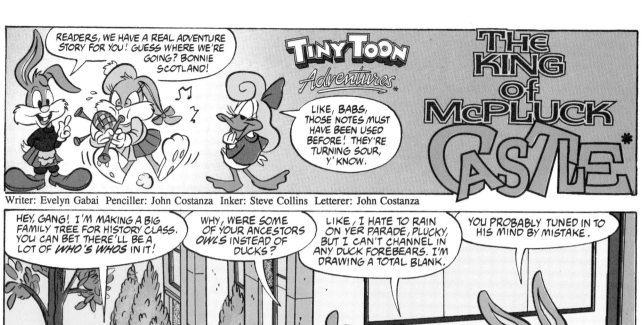

Tiny Toon Adventures*

THE KING of McPLUCK CASTLE*

Writer: Evelyn Gabai Penciller: John Costanza Inker: Steve Collins Letterer: John Costanza

6

EVEN LATER...

THEY HAVE TO KNOW ABOUT MY ANCESTORS IN THIS MUSEUM.

MUSEUM

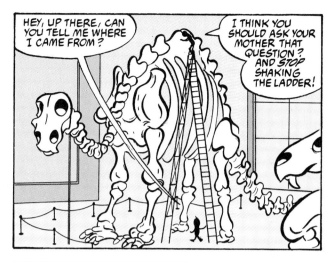

HEY, UP THERE, CAN YOU TELL ME WHERE I CAME FROM?

I THINK YOU SHOULD ASK YOUR MOTHER THAT QUESTION? AND *STOP* SHAKING THE LADDER!

I THOUGHT I TOLD YOU TO STOP-- AIIIEEEE!

TIMMBERRR!-- SORRY, THAT JUST SLIPPED OUT!

MY BEAUTIFUL GLOPPOSAURUS-- RUINED!

SHEESH, IF THE DINOSAURS WERE *THIS* BRITTLE, IT'S NO WONDER THEY'RE EXTINCT!

BY THE END OF THE DAY...

HI, PLUCKY. INSTEAD OF RIBBING YOU, WE FIGURED WE SHOULD BE SUPPORTING YOUR RESEARCH.

PLUCKY

SO, LIKE, WHAT'S WITH THE GRODY DEAD TWIG?

IT'S SUPPOSED TO BE MY FAMILY TREE. (SNIFF!) ONLY I JUST FOUND OUT I *DON'T* HAVE ANY ROOTS.

MAYBE YOU'D HAVE BETTER LUCK USING AN OAK TREE. THEY'RE FULL OF NUTS.

OH, BABS! HONESTLY, WE'RE REAL SORRY, PLUCKY. WHAT'S PAST IS PAST. UH... EXCEPT IN YOUR CASE...

NICE TRY, GUYS. BUT IF MY PAST IS EXTINCT, MY FUTURE JUST STINKS. GIVE ME *ONE* GOOD REASON WHY I *SHOULD GO ON.*

OKAY... FAN MAIL WOULD DO.

OCCUPANT AGAIN?!! I DON'T GET IT. THIS GUY GETS ALL THE MAIL, AND HE DOESN'T EVEN *LIVE* HERE!

7

WAIT--HERE'S AN OFFER TO TRACE MY ANCESTORS FOR A COAT OF ARMS.

I COULD BE DESCENDED FROM ROYALTY AFTER ALL!

AW, THAT'S JUST SOME CHEAP ATTEMPT TO GET YOUR MONEY.

OH YEAH? LOOK AT THE PRICE. BELIEVE ME, THERE'S NOTHING CHEAP ABOUT *THIS!*

YOU GUYS RUN ALONG. I'VE GOTTA CALL THESE PEOPLE RIGHT AWAY.

A WEEK LATER...

OH JOY! OH RAPTURE! MY COAT OF ARMS HAS ARRIVED!

THIS IS THE HAPPIEST DAY OF MY LIFE. I CAN'T WAIT TO SHOW IT OFF TO MY FRIENDS.

THAT VERY EVENING...

WELL, GANG, WHAT DO YOU THINK? BE HONEST.

RALPH-O-RAMA! COVER THAT BACK UP, I JUST ATE!

EXCUSE ME, BUT WHERE'RE THE ARMS YOU HANG YOUR COAT ON?

8

THERE'S A DIFFERENCE BETWEEN HONESTY AND BLUNTNESS, YOU KNOW.

IS IT ANYTHING LIKE THE DIFFERENCE BETWEEN *DRIVING* A HARD BARGAIN AND GETTING *TAKEN* FOR A *RIDE*?

REALLY PLUCKY, IS WHOEVER YOU BOUGHT THIS FROM ON THE LEVEL? HOW CAN WE BE SURE IT'S REAL?

THIS BROCHURE MAY HELP...

PLUCKY'S ANCESTORS ALSO BUILT A SCOTTISH CASTLE. HERE'S AN OFFER TO BUY BACK THE DEED.

BUT IT'S GONNA COST YOU...

FIDDLESTICKS! AT *THIS* PRICE IT'S A STEAL!

EXACTAMENTO! DON'T GIVE IN TO TEMPTATION, PLUCKY, THERE'S SOMETHING *FISHY* ABOUT THIS.

CHILL OUT, BUSTER, YOU'RE JUST SMELLING THE *FREE* BONUS GIFT *TROUT* THAT CAME IN THE BOX.

I'M GONNA BUY THAT COOL CASTLE IF IT TAKES EVERY LAST DIME I HAVE.

HOW ABOUT IT, GANG? COME TO SCOTLAND AND HELP ME CUT THE DEAL.

LIKE, THIS HAS TO BE A JOURNEY INTO THE PLANE OF SURREAL ESTATE COSMOGRAPHY-- OR SOME JUNK!

WHICH MEANS YOU'LL NEED OUR MORAL SUPPORT.

AND OUR FINANCIAL SUPPORT-- WHEN IT'S ALL OVER.

10

WHAT AN AWFUL DOWNPOUR!

DON'T BE A BUMMER, DUDE. VIEW THIS EXPERIENCE LIKE A GLASS THAT'S HALF FULL INSTEAD OF HALF EMPTY.

OKAY, SHIRL. FROM NOW ON WE'LL THINK OF OURSELVES AS HALF DROWNED.

OH, CABBY! TAKE US TO McPLUCK CASTLE, MY GOOD MAN.

AH HAH HAH HAH! THAT'S RICH!

SEE? ALREADY THE LOCALS ARE AWED BY MY WEALTH.

HMM. THAT GUY MUST BE ESPECIALLY SHY AROUND ROYALTY.

HOW DO YA FIGURE?

HE'S BOWING OUT.

NOW WHAT'RE WE SUPPOSED TO DO? WALK?

GREAT IDEA, HAMTON! I'M TOUCHED BY YOUR ENTHUSIASM!

WE'LL FOLLOW THIS ROAD. ACCORDING TO MY BROCHURE, IT LEADS STRAIGHT TO McPLUCK CASTLE.

LIKE, IS THAT ALL, YOUR MAJESTY?

NO -- MAKE SURE MY LUGGAGE STAYS OUT OF THE MUD!

AND SO OUR HEROES TRUDGE...

THROUGH DRIVING RAIN...

THROUGH BLINDING FOG...

THROUGH POUNDING SLEET...

THROUGH SLASHING HAIL...

WAIT A MINUTE, ISN'T HAIL THE *SAME* AS SLEET?

OKAY, KNOW-IT-ALL...THROUGH HEAVY *SNOW*...

THROUGH RADIOACTIVE FALLOUT...

ENOUGH ALREADY! CAN THE HARDSHIP SPECIAL EFFECTS!

OPEN UP! THE NEW KING OF MCPLUCK CASTLE HAS ARRIVED!

I'M SORRY, SIR, THERE WILL BE A SLIGHT WAIT FOR A TABLE! BUT THERE'S ROOM AT THE COUNTER!

IF YOU'RE LOOKING FOR *SNICKER* MCPLUCK CASTLE, IT'S ANOTHER MILE DOWN THE ROAD!

YOU HAVE TO ADMIT, THIS CASTLE'S HARDLY SLOPPY SECONDS, PLUCKY.

YEAH, A FEW COATS OF PURPLE STUCCO... A FLAMINGO ON THE LAWN... THEN I THINK I CAN LIVE WITH IT...

MCDOOGLE MCMAX SAID HE'D WAIT FOR ME HERE.

SO SORRY, PLUCKY! 'TIS GLAD I AM TO MEET YE!

I'M A LITTLE BOWLED OVER MYSELF...

THERE'S SOMETHING AWFULLY *FAMILIAR* ABOUT THAT GUY.

AND *SLIMY*, AND *CREEPY*...

OH BOY! WHEN CAN WE GO INSIDE, MR. MCMAX?

UHM... ER... THE MAID'S STILL CLEANING IT. LET'S SIGN THE DEED FIRST, LADDIE.

14

THIS IS THE DEAL OF A LIFETIME. BELIEVE ME -- YOUR *ENTIRE* LIFETIME.

DEED

I'LL JUST COUNT OUT WHAT I OWE YOU...

FORGET SUCH TRIFLIN'S -- WE'LL SHAKE ON IT.

HEYYY! NOW I GOTTA SEE HOW MUCH I HAVE LEFT.

NO TIME FOR THAT. SCOTTISH TRADITION SAYS WE MUST CELEBRATE WITH A HIGHLAND FLING!

UUGH! I HOPE YOU DON'T EXPECT ME TO CHANGE INTO ONE OF THOSE SKIRTS.

DON'T WORRY, LADDY. I GOT ALL THE CHANGE I NEED.

NOW THAT YOU'VE SIGNED ME IRONCLAD CONTRACT, HERE BE THE KEY TO YOUR NEW HOME.

WHAT GIVES? MY *BACK YARD'S* IN MY *LIVING ROOM!*

AYE, AND WHAT A LABOUR SAVER THAT IS NOW YE CAN WATCH TV AND MOW YOUR LAWN AT THE SAME TIME.

15

STOP, THIEF! YOU **CHEATED** ME!

BUMP

FOR PETE'S SAKE. IT'S BOG AS FAR AS THE EYE CAN SEE.

QUICK! MCMAX IS GETTING AWAY!

CRASH

YOU SOLD PLUCKY A BILL OF GOODS.

THE CASTLE'S ALL THERE, HAR! JUST NOT IN ONE PIECE!

THIS DEAL'S FAIR 'N' SQUARE -- HAH! AS ANY COUSIN OF MONTANA MAX CAN MAKE IT!

COUSIN?! OOOO! I SHOULD HAVE FELT THE SMARMY VIBES THAT RUN IN YOUR FAMILY.

WHAT YOU FELT, LASS, WAS MYSELF UPHOLDING THE MCMAX FAMILY HONOUR!

WHEN MONTY TOLD ME HOW BADLY PLUCKY WANTED A FAMILY TREE, WE DECIDED TO BUSHWHACK HIM INSTEAD!

GOOD WORK, MCMAX!

HOWDY, SUCKER! GEE, IT'S GREAT TO KNOW I CAN PULL THE WOOL OVER YOUR EYES ON TWO CONTINENTS.

16

PLUCKY'S DISASTROUS SEARCH FOR HIS ROOTS CONTINUES AS HE MEETS HIS WORST FOE... MONTANA MAX!

I SIMPLY *HAD* TO DROP BY AND LAUGH IN YOUR FACE. HARDY HAR!

IN CASE YOU WERE WONDERING, HIS BREATH *IS* AS BAD AS THE REST OF HIM.

SIGH! I CAN'T BELIEVE HOW GULLIBLE I AM!

THERE'S A WAY OUT OF THIS YET, PLUCKY.

ACCORDING TO THIS DEED, McMAX WAS ALSO SUPPOSED TO PROVIDE YOUR ANCESTORS' HISTORY.

DEED

THAT'S RIGHT! BETTER COUGH UP SOME *INFO* QUICK, McMUCK-RAKER, OR I'M HOME FREE.

YOUR HISTORY'S RIGHT HERE IN THIS BOOK OF-- *"THE WORLD'S GREATEST LOSERS"!*

FIRST, THERE WAS PLOG THE CAVE DUCK. THIS DOPE SURE WAS MISSING A LINK-- CAUSE HE INVENTED THE SQUARE WHEEL!

PLOG THE CAVE DUCK

THEN CAME ROMAN LUDICROUS AQUADUCKUS. HIS FIDDLE PLAYING STUNK SO MUCH, NERO BURNED ROME TO STOP THE NOISE!

HEY, NERO, I DO REQUESTS,

FINALLY THERE WAS...

OKAY! SHEESH, McMAX, YOU REALLY KNOW HOW TO RUIN A GUY'S DAY!

SLAM

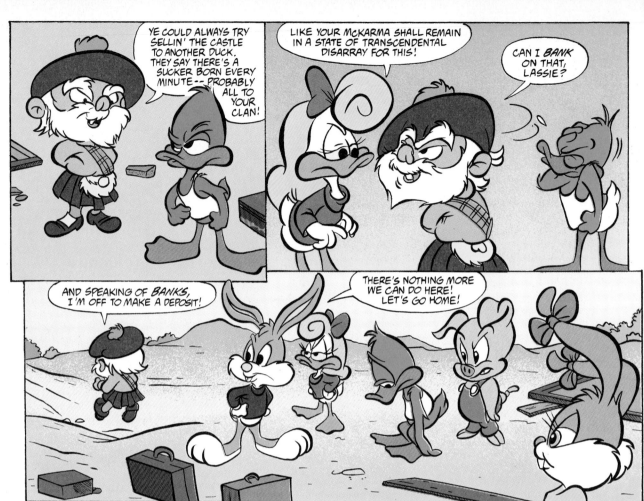

YE COULD ALWAYS TRY SELLIN' THE CASTLE TO ANOTHER DUCK. THEY SAY THERE'S A SUCKER BORN EVERY MINUTE-- PROBABLY ALL TO YOUR CLAN!

LIKE YOUR McKARMA SHALL REMAIN IN A STATE OF TRANSCENDENTAL DISARRAY FOR THIS!

CAN I *BANK* ON THAT, LASSIE?

AND SPEAKING OF *BANKS*, I'M OFF TO MAKE A DEPOSIT!

THERE'S NOTHING MORE WE CAN DO HERE! LET'S GO HOME!

I'M STAYING. THE McPLUCK NAME IS MUD SO I MIGHT AS WELL WALLOW IN IT.

PLEASE DON'T GIVE UP ON YOURSELF, PLUCKY.

WHY NOT? THE ONLY THING I'M EVER GONNA SUCCEED AT IS FAILURE. IT'S IN MY GENES.

NO PROBLEM-O. WE'LL BUY YOU A HOT NEW DESIGNER PAIR LIKE MINE!

IT'S NO USE, SHIRL. I'D BETTER ISOLATE MYSELF BEFORE MY CLAN'S CURSED KARMA RUBS OFF ON ALL OF YOU.

18

NO WAY CAN WE GO HOME NOW WITHOUT FIXING THIS MESS.

'CAUSE PLUCKY'S OUR PAL, RIGHT?

NO -- HIS LUCK'S SO BAD HE'LL CAUSE OUR PLANE TO CRASH.

SAY... LOOK AT ALL THE SUPPLIES MCMAX LEFT BEHIND! WE COULD BUILD THE CASTLE OURSELVES!

DO YA REALLY THINK WE COULD?!!

WHY NOT? MCMAX ALREADY BUILT THE FRONT FOR US.

SEE? NOW HOW CAN YOU BE A LOSER WITH GOOD FRIENDS LIKE US?

I DON'T KNOW, BUSTER, BUT HE DOES A PRETTY GOOD JOB OF IT.

SHEESH... THANKS...

OH WOW, LIKE I CAN FEEL THE LOVE FLOWING LIKE THE SLUDGE IN THIS SWAMP. CAN'T YOU?

YEAH. SURE. NOW SHADDUP AND GRAB A HAMMER.

IT'S A GOOD THING I PACKED MY ACME TOOL KIT.

LIKE, MAJOR DÉJÀ VU! DID YOU KNOW WE WERE GONNA BUILD A CASTLE?

NAH, I HEARD SCOTTISH FOOD IS REALLY TOUGH. HOW ELSE COULD I CUT MY DINNER?

IT'S YOUR CASTLE, PLUCKY. WHAT SHOULD WE BUILD FIRST? THE BALL ROOM? A TREASURE ROOM?

OR A COOL DINING ROOM?

THE BATHROOM!

IT WAS A LONG WALK FROM THAT AIRPORT, IF YOU KNOW WHAT I MEAN!

19

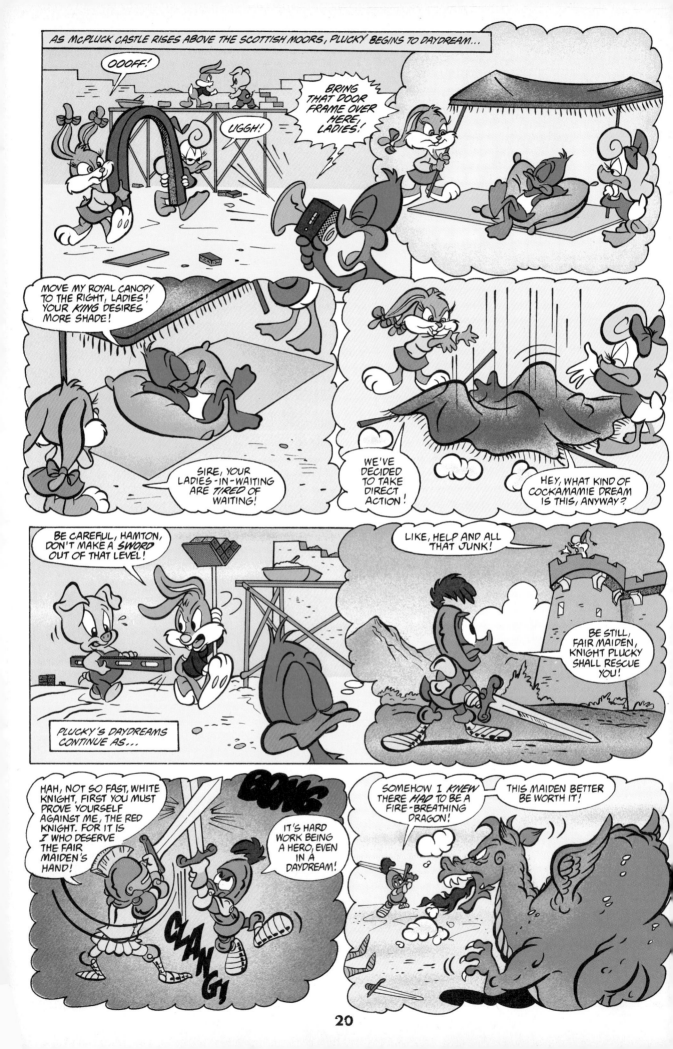

YESSIR, ONLY A TRUE McPLUCK WOULD BE LOSER ENOUGH TO BUILD HERE.

GACK!

GET A GRIP, PLUCKY. WE'RE GONNA UNLOAD THIS LEMON BACK ON THAT LOWLIFE HIGHLANDER YOU BOUGHT IT FROM.

BUT HOW?

HOW ELSE? WITH ONE OF MY SURE-FIRE PLANS...

LATER, AT McDOOGLE McMAX'S OWN ANCESTRAL HOME...

CHARITY WORKERS ENTER AT YOUR OWN RISK

WHERE ARE ALL ME CASTLE TOURISTS? COULD THEY HAVE FOUND SOME OTHER PLACE TO GO?!

OHH, I'M JUMPIN' TO SILLY CONCLUSIONS. (sigh) MAY AS WELL SEE WHAT'S ON THE TELLY.

TSK, TSK, ALL THAT DISGUSTIN' TV VIOLENCE... AND I CAN'T FIND ANY OF IT TODAY!

WHAT'S THIS?!

HEY, ALL YOU LADS 'N' LASSIES IN TV LAND! COME ON DOWN TO McPLUCK CASTLE FOR THE HOLIDAY ADVENTURE OF A LIFETIME!

YOU COUGH UP THE GREEN BILLS; WE PROVIDE THE CHEAP THRILLS! JOIN OUR MILLIONS OF HAPPY VISITORS TODAY!

OUT-SHYSTER *ME* TOURISTS FROM RIGHT UNDER ME OWN NOSE, WILL THEY?! I'LL *SEE* ABOUT THAT!

I'LL PAY 'EM A WEE VISIT IN *DISGUISE*, SO I CAN SEE WHAT ALL THE FUSS IS ABOUT.

HEH, HEH. THEY'LL NEVER RECOGNIZE ME IN THIS GET-UP.

HERE COMES OUR McPIGEON NOW. I'D *RECOGNIZE* HIM A MILLION MILES AWAY!

YEAH. THAT'S GOTTA BE THE DUMBEST DISGUISE I EVER SAW.

LIKE, I'LL SAY, DOESN'T HE REALIZE HOW BADLY PRINTS CLASH WITH PLAIDS?

MAN YOUR BATTLE STATIONS, GANG!

WELCOME TO McPLUCK CASTLE, THE MOST FUN PLACE ON EARTH.

AND THE MOST EXPENSIVE. FIFTY POUNDS ADMISSION, PLEASE.

WE'RE YOUR LOVABLE CARTOON CHARACTER HOSTS, SKIMMY AND SKAMMY SKUNK.

YOU'LL RIDE IN THIS CART FOR THE ENTIRE TOUR, SIR.

BUT I HAD PLANS TO SPY...ER, SAUNTER AROUND.

THE OLD SKUNK SMELL GETS 'EM EVERY TIME!

23

YOU SQUIRRELY SKUNKS BETTER SHOW ME SOMETHING GOOD!

WHAAAAAAA

RELAX, IT'S ONLY CASTLE MCPLUCKS' *TORTURE CHAMBER.*

WHAT A RELIEF! FOR A MINUTE I THOUGHT I WAS BACK IN THIRD GRADE.

HOW DO YOU LIKE OUR CASTLE DUNGEON SO FAR?

I LOVE IT!

YOU DO?

MUST WE GO? I'M REALLY HAVING FUN HERE!

OTHER GUESTS ARE COMING. WE'VE GOT TO MAKE ROOM!

MMMM. WHAT UNBELIEVABLE EATIN'S.

URP! ME COMPLIMENTS TO YOU THE CHEF.

I'M NOT THE CHEF, I'M THE ARTIST WHO CREATED THE *WAX* FOOD DISPLAY YOU JUST ATE!

WAX OR NAE, IT'S BONNIE GOOD! I WANT THE RECIPES!

SURE, BUT MEANWHILE WE HAVE LOTS MORE TO SHOW YOU!

24

THIS IS OUR INDOOR AMERICAN FOOTBALL STADIUM. NEXT YEAR, WE'RE HOSTING THE WORLD CUP!

MIGHTY IMPRESSIVE.

PROGRAMMES! YOU CAN'T TELL THE PLAYERS WITHOUT A PROGRAMME!

HOT DOGS! GET 'EM WHILE THEY'RE HOT!

WE HAVE OUR OWN CONVENTION CENTRE!

VINTAGE GOLDEN-AGE COMICS! MINT CONDITION!

NOT TO MENTION A ROCKET CONTROL BASE.

FOR OUR RICHER GUESTS WHO'VE BEEN AROUND THE WORLD SO MANY TIMES, AND ARE LOOKING FOR SOMEPLACE *ELSE* TO GO.

ME HEAD IS REELIN'! I CAN'T BELIEVE YE BUILT THIS ALL IN ONE DAY!

THAT WAS EASY. NOW WE COME TO THE PIÈCE DE RÉSISTANCE, OUR PRIDE AND JOY.

AH, THE BONNIE SHORES OF LOCH McPLUCK.

HOME OF THE FAMOUS McPLUCK SEAMONSTER.

McSEAMONSTER? HAH! WHAT DO YE TAKE ME FOR, LASSIE?

HOPEFULLY EVERY DIME WE CAN GET.

THEIR BOAT IS JUST ABOVE US NOW. PREPARE TO SURFACE THE MONSTER!

AYE, AYE, CAPTAIN PLUCKY.

SOMETIME LATER...

SO WHAT'S WITH THIS "*I'M GONNA BE RICH*" STUFF, BUDDY?

THIS IS PLUCKY'S CASTLE!

YES, AND I'M JUST A HUMBLE TOURIST WHO'S COME BEGGIN' TO BUY IT FROM HIM.

TOURIST MY LUCKY RABBIT'S FOOT. YOU'RE MCDOOGLE MCMAX.

WELL I'M NOT THE ONLY ONE WHO STINKS O' DECEPTION AROUND HERE, "*SKUNKS.*"

HAH! OR SHOULD I SAY-- *BUNNIES!*

BUT I FORGIVE THE LOT OF YE. I JUST WANT MCPLUCK CASTLE BACK! I'D SELL YE MY VERY *SOUL* FOR IT.

SORRY, I DON'T DEAL IN THAT KIND OF CHEAP, *SLEAZY* MERCHANDISE.

NAME YER PRICE, DUCK.

I'LL LET YOU HAVE IT FOR WHAT I PAID FOR IT.

WAIT, I SOLD YOU *HALF* A CASTLE, AND NOW I'M GETTIN' A *WHOLE* ONE FOR THE SAME PRICE? MCPLUCK, THERE'S ONLY ONE WORD TO DESCRIBE YE.

LOSER! LOSER! LOSER!

PARDON ME, MCDOOGLE, THAT'S THREE WORDS.

IT'S BEEN A REAL PLEASURE DOIN' BUSINESS WITH YE. NOW *GIT OFF* ME PROPERTY, YE TRESPASSIN' SWINE!

28

BUSTER'S BRAIN BUSTER

Can you find three groups of things that have something in common?

Script: Robert Leighton   Art: Nate Butler

ACME ART LESSON 7

Welcome to the unveiling of my new invention, the Computerized Logistical Image-Converting Kinescope, or CLICK. It's the last word in high-focus photography! It's not merely a camera. It's not simply an instamatic. In fact, I'm not sure what it is — but it's gonna make me rich, rich, *rich!*

To demonstrate the superiority of the Compterized Logistical Image Converting Kinescope, my first victim — er, artistic subject — will be Calamity Coyote.

While we're waiting for the Computerized Logistical Image-Converting Kinescope to process Calamity's picture, let me show you how to draw him yourself.

You don't have to draw the whole face at once. Just start with a circle and crossing lines, like you see here. Then add the eyes, ears, nose, and mouth. Finally, add the details and colour them in — and you've developed his picture yourself! Now, let's take a look at what CLICK has done.

Script: Rob Dinsmoor Art: Jim Bresnahan and Frank McLaughlin

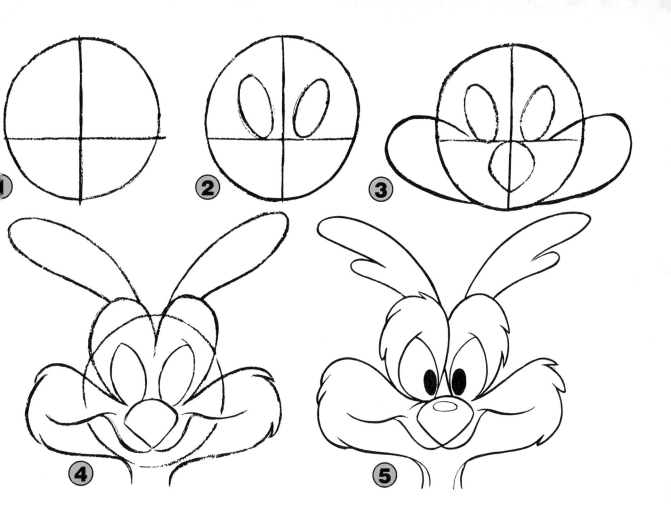

Yipe! The focus is a little *too* sharp! I must have used *X-ray* film by mistake!

SEARCH FOR BURIED TREASURE

Script: John Albano   Art: Joe Messerli

33

Writer: Nicholas Hollander   Penciller: Chuck Fiala   Inker: Scott McRae   Letterer: Ken Leach

WB-27

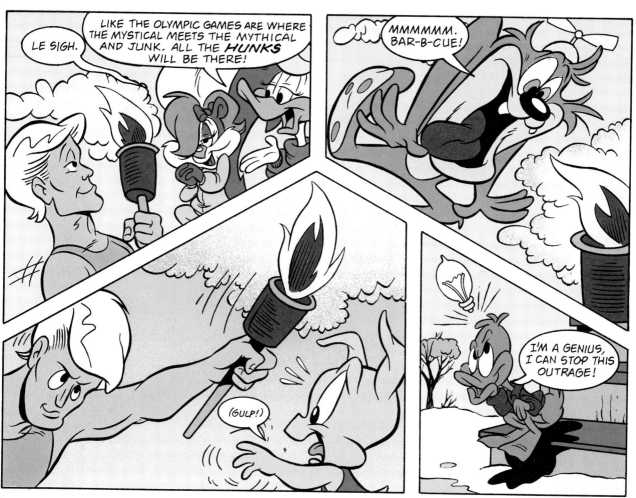

35

OOMPH!

MAYBE THIS WASN'T SUCH A GOOD IDEA!

HEY, LEFTY! SINCE WHEN DO PIGS HAVE FEATHERS???

QUIT CALLING ME LEFTY. MY NAME'S PETE!

THOSE HIJACKERS DIDN'T RECKON ON MY ATHLETIC ABILITY.

HEY! MAYBE THEY'LL MAKE BAG RACING AN OLYMPIC EVENT!

RIP

THE GOLD MEDAL WOULD LOOK GREAT AROUND MY NECK...

RIP

...AS I STAND AT ATTENTION WHILE THE BAND PLAYS THE ACME ACRES ANTHEM JUST FOR ME!

I WISH I KNEW WHERE I AM.

BONK

owww!

HIPPETTY HOP HOP

GOOD. I CAN USE THIS TREE AS A LANDMARK!

HEY, THAT SOUNDED LIKE PLUCKY!

THAT DIRTY DUCK! WAIT'TIL I GET MY HANDS ON HIM!

PLUCKY! WHAT HAPPENED?

WHERE'S THE TORCH?

I WAS BUSHWHACKED THEY STOLE THE TORCH!

THE TORCH IS GONE?

HOW CAN THERE BE ANY WINTER OLYMPICS WITHOUT THE FLAME?

ACME ACRES WILL *NEVER* LIVE THIS DOWN!

IT'S ALL YOUR FAULT!

THAT'S RIGHT! BLAME THE VICTIM!

WHO DID IT, PLUCKY?

I DON'T KNOW. IT WAS DARK. BUT THERE WERE AT LEAST FIVE BIG BRUISERS!

THIS SITUATION CALLS FOR A LITTLE *BUNNY INGENUITY...*

LET'S GIVE IT A WHIRL, BABS!

AND IN THE TWINKLING OF AN EYE...

BUSTER AND BABS BUNNY-- PRIVATE EYES!

NO RELATION...

WHO WOULD BE SO *SELFISH AND CON-NIVING* TO STEAL THE GREAT OLYMPIC SYMBOL?

SELFISH. CONNIVING. DID WE SAY *GREEDY* AND SNIVELLING...?

IT'S MINE! MINE! *MINE!*

38

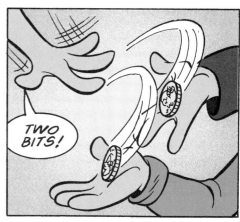

WHAT DO WE DO NOW?

IMPROVISE. SOMETHING WILL COME. IT ALWAYS DOES...

MON-EY

IT'S PROBABLY A PATHETIC CHARITY WORKER LOOKING FOR A HANDOUT. I'LL TAKE CARE OF HIM.

VERY GOOD, SIR.

HI! I'M DAN DEEP...

AND I'M DEBBIE SHALLOW. WE HOST THAT WONDERFUL NEW TV SHOW, "AT HOME WITH THE WEALTHY AND UNHAPPY." WE'D LOVE TO FEATURE YOU ON OUR UPCOMING SHOW, MR. MAX.

IT'S ABOUT TIME THAT CRUMMY PROGRAMME OF YOURS GOT A LITTLE CLASS!

LET ME BEGIN BY SHOWING YOU MY CARRARA MARBLE BATHROOM WITH SOLID GOLD FIXTURES AND AIR-CONDITIONED SAUNA...

HOW ABOUT SHOWING US YOUR LATEST ACQUISITION?

OH, NEVER MIND THAT, YOU REALLY MUST SEE MY INDOOR 80-METRE SKI JUMP!

FANTASTIC, ISN'T IT! YOU KNOW, I BID ON THE 1992 WINTER OLYMPICS.

ALBERTVILLE WILL BE SORRY THEY OUTBID ME!

WELL, DAN AND DEBBIE, THAT'S THE END OF THE TOUR. WHAT DO YOU THINK? WHEN WILL YOUR CREW BE OVER TO SHOOT?

BUT WE HAVEN'T EVEN SEEN THE UPSTAIRS YET!

COME BACK HERE, THERE'S NOTHING UP THERE!

BEEP BEEP BEEP BEEP BEEP

WHAT'S THAT NOISE?

UHH...THAT'S JUST MY BEEPER. I MUST HAVE A PHONE CALL.

NO, THE NOISE SEEMS TO BE COMING FROM DOWN THE HALL.

PRIVATE!

NO PEEKING

UH...UH! MUSTN'T TOUCH!

BACK, I SAY!

IT'S COMING FROM INSIDE!

STAY AWAY FROM THAT DOOR!

SORRY, SIR, THERE SEEMS TO BE A SLIGHT SHORT IN THE CIRCUIT.

YOUR ELECTRICIAN PROMISED HE'D BE HERE TWO WEEKS AGO. BUT YOU KNOW HOW HARD IT IS TO FIND GOOD HELP THESE DAYS, SIR.

DARN, THEY FORGOT TO TELL ME WHEN THEY'RE GOING TO SHOOT MY SEGMENT.

AND TOONY...

MONTE THINKS HE'S TRICKED US.

WELL, WE MAY BE TINY...

BUT WE'RE NOT ALL THAT *LOONEY!* WE KNOW WHERE THAT TORCH IS!!

GOOD WORK, SNODLEY! YOU DESERVE A *REWARD.*

THAT'S VERY GENEROUS OF YOU, SIR MONTY...

TOO BAD YOU'RE NOT GETTING ONE!

HEH, HEH, HEH...

I BET ACME ACRES MADE HEADLINES TONIGHT!

WORLD NEWS

DISTURBING NEWS GREETED THE WORLD TODAY, AS THE OLYMPIC TORCH, ON ITS WAY TO ALBERTVILLE, WAS HIJACKED! IN OUR STUDIO TONIGHT IS THE VICTIM OF THIS TERRIBLE CRIME.

GOOD EVENING...

HI! PLUCKY DUCK HERE! I WAS PROUDLY BEARING THE OLYMPIC TORCH, WHEN OUT OF THE SHADOWS, I WAS SET UPON BY--

YES, YES, WHO TOOK THE TORCH? CAN YOU IDENTIFY HIM?

HIM? THERE WERE AT LEAST A DOZEN OF THEM! I FOUGHT WITH THE STRENGTH OF TEN, BUT THEY EVENTUALLY OVERCAME ME!

ELSEWHERE...

SACRE BLEU! IT HAD TO BE A COUNTRY THAT PUT IN A BID AND LOST TO LA FRANCE.

I SAY, THIS IS A RUM POT OF TEA, WHAT?

...AND I INTEND TO CALL FOR A FULL CONGRESSIONAL INVESTIGATION OF THIS OUTRAGE!

IT'S A DIRTY CAPITALIST PLOT! WHAT BECAME OF FRIENDSHIP?

"MEANWHILE, IN ALBERTVILLE, THE ATHLETES ARE A DEJECTED LOT. UNTIL THE TORCH IS RECOVERED, THE WINTER OLYMPICS *CANNOT* BEGIN."

AS YET, THERE IS NO CLUE AS TO WHO IS RESPONSIBLE FOR THIS THEFT.

BUT WE KNOW, DON'T WE, BUSTER?

RIGHT ON, BABSIE! IT'S TIME TO ACT, BUNNY STYLE!

44

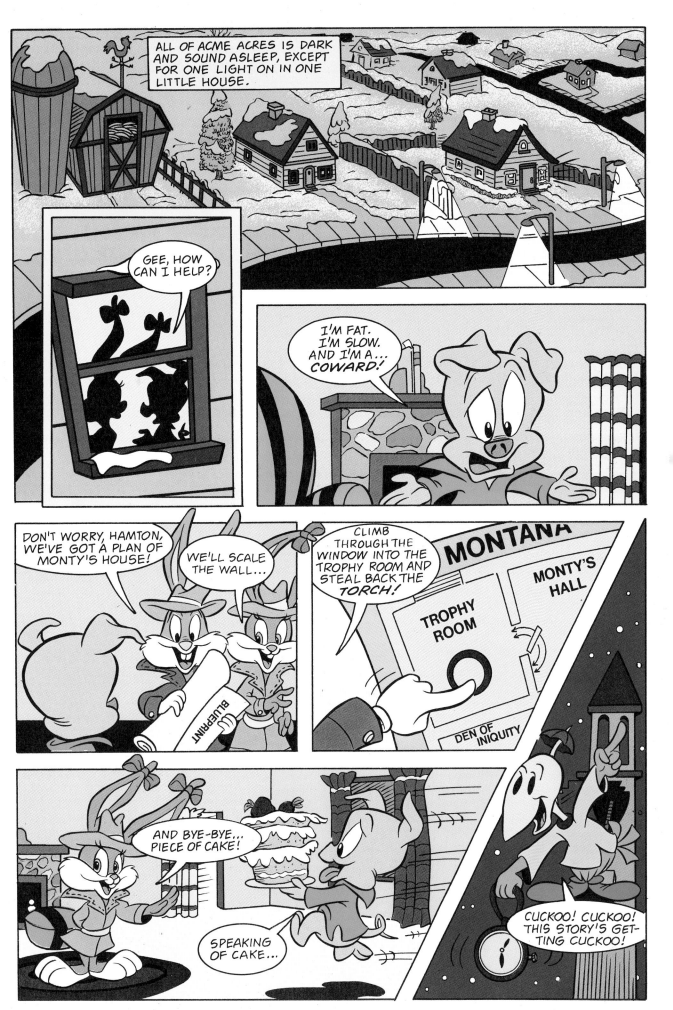

RISKING LIFE AND LIMB TO RESCUE THE OLYMPIC TORCH, BUSTER, BABS AND HAMTON PREPARE TO SNEAK INTO MONTY'S MANSION.

SHHHHHHH!

NIGHT WATCHMAN

NO TRESPASSING

ZZZZZZZZ-ZZZZZZ...

THESE SUCTION CUP SHOES WILL MAKE US STICK LIKE GLUE.

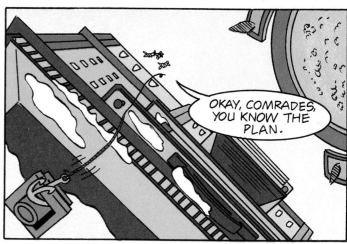

OKAY, COMRADES, YOU KNOW THE PLAN.

DID I EVER TELL YOU GUYS I'M AFRAID OF HEIGHTS?

MAYBE THIS WASN'T A GOOD IDEA...?

46

47

AND SO IT FOLLOWS...

HERE'S THE PLAN, MEN. I KNOW THOSE STUPID TOONS ARE ON THEIR WAY TO ALBERTVILLE. WE'LL BUSHWHACK THEM THERE!

THEY DON'T HAVE TASMANIAN DEVILS THERE, DO THEY?

OH, QUIT YOUR BELLYACHING AND SUIT UP!

AFTER ALL, WOULD I LEAD YOU INTO DANGER? WE'RE A TEAM!

ONE FOR ALL, AND ALL FOR...

ME!

WE'VE BEEN TRAVELLING FOR DAYS! CAN'T WE STOP FOR BRUNCH?

NOT UNTIL WE REACH ALBERT-VILLE.

LOOK UP AHEAD, BUSTER--THAT BILLBOARD!

TWO SCRAMBLED EGGS. HOLD THE BACON.

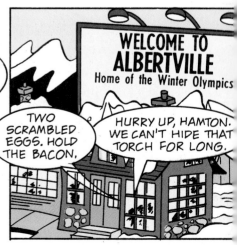

WELCOME TO ALBERTVILLE
Home of the Winter Olympics

HURRY UP, HAMTON. WE CAN'T HIDE THAT TORCH FOR LONG.

I'M NOT FINISHED YET! I'LL GET MY TORCH BACK! THEY'VE STILL GOT TO GET TO THE STADIUM!

IMAGINE COMING ALL THIS WAY-- AND NO GAMES!

I'M TOO DEPRESSED EVEN TO PRACTISE.

THE OLYMPIC VILLAGE IN ALBERTVILLE IS A SCENE OF TOTAL GLOOM. THE WORLD HAS GIVEN UP HOPE THAT THE MISSING TORCH WILL EVER BE FOUND.

LOOK AT ALL THOSE DUMMIES IN THE STADIUM! THEY KNOW THE TORCH IS MISSING, BUT THEY CAME ANYWAY!

WHAT A BUNCH OF LOSERS!

BUSTER THINKS HE'S TRICKED ME! HAH! WE'LL TAKE THEM ON ONE ON ONE!

THERE THEY ARE-- THREE SMOKE TRAILS! BAIL OUT! WE'LL EACH TAKE A DIFFERENT TOON.

IS THAT FIFTY-PENCE REWARD STILL GOOD?

MEN, I'M NOT GONNA TELL YOU AGAIN-- *GET THAT TORCH!*

I GOT YOU, PIG!

HUFF... PUFF...

SURPRISE! HAPPY BIRTHDAY!

WHADDAYA TALKIN' ABOUT? IT AIN'T MY BIRTHDAY!

OKAY, SWEETHEART! I'LL TAKE THAT TORCH!

FOOLED YOU, DIDN'T I?

SMOG

COUGH, COUGH

IT'S THE END OF THE LINE, BUNNY! GIVE ME BACK MY TORCH!

MONTY, IT ISN'T RIGHT TO STEAL THE OLYMPIC TORCH. IT BELONGS TO THE WORLD!

ASK ME IF I CARE!

HAND IT OVER!

NEVER!

NO SKATING

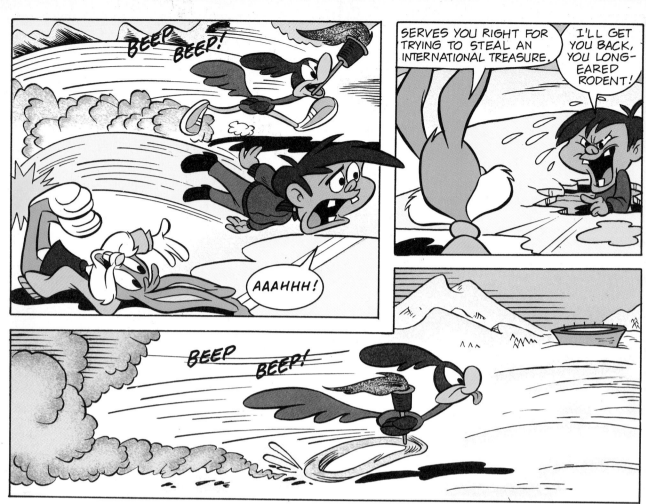

BEEP BEEP!

AND NOW WE WILL HAVE THE LIGHTING OF THE OLYMPIC FLAME...

...MARKING THE OFFICIAL OPENING OF THE 1992 WINTER GAMES.

LET THE GAMES BEGIN!

HOORAY!

THAT SHOULD HAVE BEEN *ME* LIGHTING THE FLAME. BUT NO-OOO! THEY HAD TO GIVE THE JOB TO THAT *SPEED DEMON.*

WE *DID* IT! WE RESCUED THE TORCH FROM MONTANA MAX AND SAVED THE OLYMPICS!

SPEAKING OF MAX, HERE HE COMES.

JUST WAIT 'TIL THE SUMMER GAMES! I'LL BE BACK!

WHEN I THAW OUT!

IN YOUR DREAMS, PAL!

THE END

57

Calamity Coyote's REALLY WEIRD Science Project

NAME:

SCHOOL:

GRADE:

Robert Leighton Art: Dan Loprieno and John Costanza

Calamity Coyote has lured Little Beeper to his laboratory, where he will now shrink him to a more edible size. But if Calamity wasn't a mad scientist to begin with, he'll certainly be mad once his little set-up backfires, as usual! Here's how it works:

Calamity **A** throws switch **B** sending juice along wires **C** to batteries **D** . The resulting lightning bolt **E** bursts nearby chain **F** , releasing long-tethered Space Alien **G** . Space Alien runs along treadmill **H** , attached to clock **I** , which spins backwards. Chicken **J** , thinking a time-travel experiment is occurring, dives back into egg **K** , upsetting teeterboard **L** and springing vial of Jekyll Hyde serum **M** in front of fuzzy little rabbit **N** . Little rabbit becomes ferocious, monstrous rabbit **O** who tears open the bars of the cage, tipping jar **P** , and sending Bad Brain **Q** into Frankenstein-like monster. Monster instinctively raises arms **R** , pulling cord **S** which upsets pitcher of water **T** . Water nourishes Ravenous Plant From Another World **U** which quickly grows to full height **V** . Ravenous Plant tries to eat Start Button **W** , firing up super-charged Copy Machine **X** , which is supposed to reduce Little Beeper like a piece of paper. However, Little Beeper holds up mirror **Y** , which focuses Shrink-Light back onto Calamity Coyote, shrinking him instead **Z** ! And now Calamity's a very appetizing size for Space Alien, Ferocious Rabbit, Frankenstein, and Ravenous Plant!

ACME LOONIVERSITY
FINAL EXAM

Buster Bunny
is leading an expedition through the
dark and dangerous jungle. But the animals have camouflaged
themselves so well that Buster doesn't sense any danger at all! Can you find,
hidden in this scene, the alligator, bat, centipede, giraffe, lion, octopus,
rhino, shark and snake?

Gogo Dodo is fully prepared for his trip to a place that gets more than nine feet of rain every year! What kind of place would that be?

Can you figure out where Plucky Duck is off to? This is the strange message he left!

Hint: If you can't figure it out, read the message to a friend!

Sea eye are
see you ess

Script: Robert Leighton   Art: Dave Concepcion and Tad Chow